The Royal Scottish National Hospital
140 Years

The Royal Scottish National Hospital

140 Years

Guthrie Hutton

Forth Valley Primary Care NHS Trust
2000

Working in the fields.

© 2000 Forth Valley Primary Care NHS Trust

First Published in the United Kingdom, 2000
by
Forth Valley Primary Care NHS Trust,
Old Denny Road,
Larbert FK5 4SD.

ISBN 0 953936 80 5

Printed by
Cordfall Ltd
0141 572 0878

Contents

Dr Brodie and his mother-in-law donated these first pennies for the Institution. They were kept as mementoes, 'lost' and then rediscovered in 1981 – in the hospital safe!

The Idea is Born

Across Europe, in the 1830s and 40s, attitudes were changing towards people with a mental handicap. Care and education were being pioneered in Paris and Switzerland, while Britain's first school was set up in Bath by two sisters. It had four pupils. Magazine articles describing all this work were published in Edinburgh in 1847 at the instigation of a Dr John Coldstream who led a debate calling for a training school to be set up in Scotland. His plea was taken up by Sir John and Lady Ogilvie who gave over part of their Baldovan Estate near Dundee. Their school was opened in 1855 as was another in Gayfield Square, Edinburgh, where a Dr and Mrs Brodie provided the children's education.

A portrait of Dr Coldstream which hung in the Institution's boardroom. The Chinese characters on the scroll point to missionary work done prior to his campaign for a school.

This all happened against a background of growing awareness of the needs of people with mental problems. At the time, a variety of private asylums and homes provided care, at a price. Poor people had to fend for themselves or endure various forms of imprisonment. The Poor Law Amendment Act of 1845 began a process of change. It charged Parish Councils with providing places in poorhouses, or paying for asylum accommodation.

Conditions in asylums, however, failed to impress a visiting American social reformer, Dorothea Dix. She had influenced changes in the treatment of mentally ill people in the USA and Canada, and reported what she had found in Scotland to the Home Office. They reacted by setting up a Royal Commission in 1855 to enquire into the country's mental health provision.

The Commissioner's report formed the basis of the Lunacy (Scotland) Act of 1857, which set a standard for future mental health legislation. It also provided for a General Board of Commissioners in Lunacy – the forerunner of the Mental Health Commission. Their task was to oversee the implementation of the Act, and they took to it with zeal, pushing, cajoling and sometimes bullying Parish Councils, and private asylums, to shape up.

The new law did not distinguish between mental handicap and mental illness, or make separate provision for children, but in their first annual report the Commissioners' referred to the work of what they called 'Idiot Schools' at Baldovan and Gayfield Square. They noted the 'earnest efforts being made by the Directors of the (Gayfield Square) school, and other persons' to raise funds for a model institution in the Edinburgh area. It was a reference to the Society for Education of Imbecile Youth in Scotland which had been formed in 1859, but if the Commissioners doubted its likely success, they underestimated the members' determination.

The Society raised money through public appeals and personal contacts, but it was a slow process and the school had to move from Gayfield Square to a smaller house at Colinton Bank, where fewer pupils could be taken in. More money was needed and, if it could not be raised more quickly, there was a danger that the project would lose momentum. A 'big idea' was needed: it came in the form of a penny subscription, a simple scheme thought to have been devised by Mrs Brodie. Instead of a few people donating large sums of money, many people would give a small sum. It worked: as the pennies rolled in from all over Scotland the pounds began to accumulate. About £1,500 was raised, and to this was added a legacy of £500. Within a short space of time the Society had become a major charitable body. A board of directors was set up and, in February 1862, public meetings were held in Edinburgh and Glasgow. Local committees and Ladies' Auxiliaries were formed, and fund-raising efforts were stepped up. A bazaar, held in Edinburgh over three days between Christmas 1862 and the New Year, raised nearly £800 – a huge sum for the time!

The Society had already made moves to set up a school. The directors looked for a house or land near Edinburgh, but met opposition when they declared their purpose and had to go further afield. In 1861 they obtained a five-acre site on Stenhouse Estate near Larbert. It was beside the railway, about three-quarters of a mile north of the station, and was ideal for an institution intended to cater for the whole of Scotland. The Scottish Central Railway had reached the little village of Larbert in 1848 and transformed it into a strategically important centre. Rails converged on it from all over the country: vital for the new Institution, because building materials, supplies and, eventually, people could get to it from almost anywhere.

The architect Frederick T. Pilkington was engaged to design the new school. He had achieved recent fame by winning competitions to design the Trinity Free Church in Irvine and the Barclay Church in Bruntsfield Place, Edinburgh. Pilkington favoured strong Gothic forms which he achieved to dramatic effect with the Barclay Church: its spire was the tallest structure in Scotland when completed. Before he put pen to paper he visited institutions in England to learn about the subject. He then drew up plans for a group of buildings where up to two hundred children could be cared for and educated. The focal point was to be a large house for the Resident Physician and private, fee-paying, pupils.

The availability of funds dictated the pace of construction. Work began in September 1861 on a dormitory block. It was completed in May 1863. The building could hold up to thirty pupils, but initially just nine moved in from the Edinburgh home, along with Dr Brodie who became the first Resident Physician. When they arrived, construction of the main house was under way. The directors had wanted it to be ready as soon as possible and had given the go-ahead in July 1862, despite having less than half the money available to pay for it. They were, however, so confident of reaching their target that they gave the bank personal security to avoid taking out an expensive loan. The house was finished by 1864, but it could not be occupied until more money was found to buy furniture.

The new establishment was called the Scottish National Institution for the Education of Imbecile Children, although the word 'National' was not part of the name for the first two years. It was intended for children between six and twelve years old, but soon younger and older children were being admitted. Children were not normally expected to stay for more than five years, but some remained at the Institution until they were young adults.

Initially, there was no provision for state-aided pupils and so a variety of admission criteria were applied. Preference was given to children likely to benefit from care and education. A child whose family could afford to pay the whole cost was admitted at the directors' discretion, and at times even children from overseas countries were accepted. Children whose families could only pay part of the fees were admitted, with the Institution meeting the balance, which varied from child to child. They gained entry after being elected by the subscribers from a list of suitable applicants. Subscribers were able to cast a number of votes depending on the size of their donation, and although lobbying to persuade them to vote for a particular child was common, it was frowned on by the directors. This election process eventually became too cumbersome and was stopped. The directors also had discretion to admit children from families who made little or no financial contribution. They made up a third of the 'elected' pupils, and the Society bore the cost of their stay at the Institution. At times, the directors admitted very young children, believing it important to start their education at the earliest stage, and also admitted less easily educable children to 'relieve families of the burden'.

The Institution.

To begin with, the Institution, like the house at Colinton, was unlicensed. Dr Brodie and the directors were concerned about having to comply with inappropriate lunacy laws, but they were also deterred by the cost – fifteen pounds, ten shillings. This concern was removed by the Lunacy (Scotland) Act of 1862, which made it lawful for a licence to be granted, at no cost 'to any charitable institution established for the care and training of imbecile children'. But the directors remained wary about the Board of Lunacy's regulatory authority, even after they had accepted it.

As the Institution got down to work, some problems emerged. The separate buildings were difficult to heat and the individual catering facilities were costly and inefficient. A new plan was drawn up to link the structures together. The directors hoped this would make it easier to expand the accommodation, make the benefits of the home available to more children and generate more income. Their ideas began to diverge from those of Dr Brodie, who wanted more staff and facilities to deal with fewer children on a more personal level. The two views were irreconcilable and this dedicated pioneer resigned on 31st December 1867. He and his wife settled in Liberton, where they continued to take in children, the first seven of whom went with them from Larbert. Dr Brodie was succeeded by Dr Adam Addison, who resigned in November 1870 and was succeeded by Dr William W. Ireland.

The number of children grew steadily – 43 in 1867, 59 in 1868, 65 in 1869 and 75 in 1870. More dormitories, class rooms and service facilities were added. The variety of activities was expanded and included outdoor work, carpentry, tailoring and shoemaking. Boys and girls were put in separate classes, which allowed boys to be given 'more manly' drill, but spoiled the harmony of singing lessons!

The money to pay for the expansion and running of the Institution continued to come from charitable donations. In October 1869, as part of their continuing search for new benefactors, the directors wrote to Queen Victoria. Within days they had a letter from the Keeper of Her Majesty's Privy Purse enclosing a cheque for £100. It was the first of annual royal donations, which were later increased to £150.

Within ten years, the fund-raising society had become a respected institution supported by royalty. But for those associated with it, the work had only just begun.

'One of our most excellent charities'

A journalist, writing in 1873, described the Institution as 'one of our most excellent charities'. At the time it was new and newsworthy, and articles by visiting writers have left an interesting picture of it. First impressions for one scribe were of flowers bordering the walk to the main entrance. Buttercups and daisies grew in the playgrounds, which were of grass, not gravel, so that children could tumble on them in safety.

In 1869, just before the new buildings were ready to be occupied, one writer described the dormitories as lofty, well ventilated rooms, and models of cleanliness and comfort. Linen was spotless, children had their own beds and an attendant slept in every room. Children had to say their prayers night and morning, and a large number attended church on Sundays. The dining room was small, but the sick room was large and comfortable, and although there were some toys, donations of more would be welcomed.

He wrote in admiration about the way children, without any sense of what was going on around them, were watched for signs of animation that could be carefully nurtured and built upon. Likening the process to making a fire, he described how the spark was tenderly fed and gently fanned until a tiny flickering flame appeared. That was the hardest part, and once it was overcome the flame could be made to grow brighter until the child was ready to attend the school. Children were put through their exercises together and the schoolmistress used kindness, rather than fear, to motivate her charges.

Initially, there was only one schoolroom, but as numbers increased more rooms were added. Educational capacities were split into five grades, from those who could neither speak nor understand, to those who could read books for themselves. There

The impressive approach to the Institution, although early visitors would have seen it without mature trees.

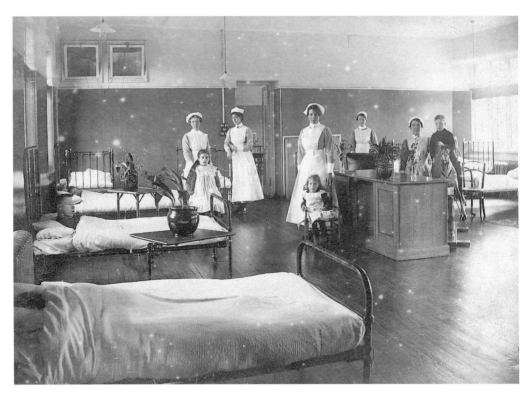

Dormitories, 'models of cleanliness and comfort' in 1869 and, as here, in the early twentieth century.

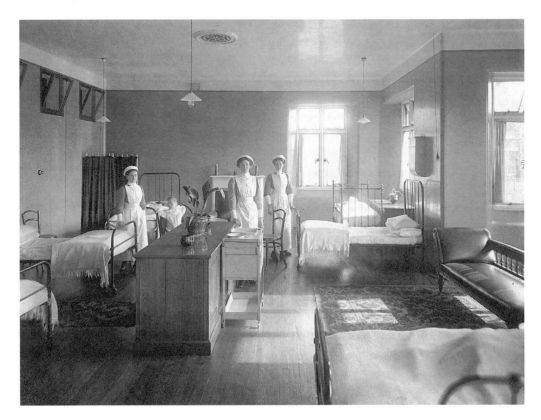

was much ingenuity in the teaching of the colour, form and weight of objects, the value of money and how to tell the time. Some children learned to copy out of a copybook – one writer thought the work done by the girls 'would pass muster in any school'. Reading was taught by memory – first, learning words by repetition, then following them in a lesson book. Only when letters were fixed in the child's mind was the combined alphabet attempted. Some also learned arithmetic. Girls and boys sewed; so well that all of the Institution's needlework was done by them. Some of the boys showed an aptitude for fancy needlework.

A bell summoned the children to the dinner room. It was a spacious hall with church-like windows and roof, and neatly laid tables. Broth followed by minced meat and rice were supplied in good quantities by the waiting officials. The more able children helped weaker companions to eat. The meal was followed by a music lesson to the accompaniment of a splendid piano, a gift to the Institution.

After lunch the girls went to do household chores or returned to the schoolroom to sew and knit. They made handkerchiefs, pinafores, chemises, knitted articles and delicately executed pieces of fancy work. The boys went to the workshops. Some made boats, stools and a variety of tools and implements in the joiner's shop. Others helped to mend shoes or make brushes or doormats: 270 brushes, 30 door mats and 72 grain sacks were made over a year in the early 1870s. Some boys sawed and chopped firewood, while many of them worked with the gardener because this was a likely source of employment when they left.

Drill at half-past-four ended the day's work and the children occupied the hours until bedtime with amusements like football, cricket and croquet. There was a children's dog, a retriever called Wallace, and other pets like goldfish and caged canaries.

The neatly laid tables of the dinner hall.

Children on the long verandah, erected in 1910.

On to the Twentieth Century

By 1875, the number of children had risen to 95, but the directors felt that the Institution was not finished and employed an architect to draw up plans to extend the buildings. They launched another appeal for funds and a 'friend' promised £200 if four others did likewise. The new wing was completed by 1877, raising the residential capacity of the buildings to over 200, but it was some years before they could be furnished and fully occupied. The old east wing was allocated to girls and small boys, and the new west wing to the older boys – there were always more mentally handicapped boys than girls.

In 1876, before the new wings were opened, the Institution faced an awkward reality. The Commissioners in Lunacy had indicated that allowing children over eighteen years of age to remain at the Institution might be illegal. It was; some older children were discharged, and the upper age limit was fixed.

Dr Ireland, who wrote one of the first British text books on mental deficiency, in 1877, resigned at the end of March 1881. The directors departed from precedent by appointing a non-medical Superintendent, Alexander Skene, to succeed him. They also appointed a Medical Officer, Dr Hamilton, but he died the following year and was replaced by Dr George Leslie. He died in 1893 and was replaced by Dr Durward Clarkson, whose appointment was to prove inspired.

Alex Skene presided over a period of almost continuous growth. When he arrived, 25 staff cared for about 120 children: when he left there were more than 350 children and 70 staff. In his time new furnishings and ornaments were put in. Some out-of-date rooms were converted into a new hall, and bay windows were added. New schoolrooms were built, which allowed children of different levels to be separated, and the nursery was enlarged to take 20 children. New buildings were erected, including an infectious diseases hospital, gatehouse-lodge, covered playground, sanatorium and staff cottages. Additional land was purchased to replace the ground lost to building.

By 1892 the Institution was caring for more children than it was licensed for and so an application was made to the Commissioners in Lunacy for an increase from 180 to 230. But numbers continued to rise and further application was made in 1897 to raise the limit to 270. Sixteen ineducable Glasgow children were sent to Woodilee Hospital when its new home for such children opened in 1900, but the space was soon filled and numbers continued to rise. The Commissioners expressed concern, and in response a new dormitory block for 50 pupils was built. It was opened in 1907 and brought the numbers that could be accommodated up to 350 which, according to one Director, was 'as much as an establishment of that kind should have'.

The telephone was installed in 1894. Electric light was put into the new block, sanatorium and laundry in 1907, but the original

Boys' day room looking onto the long verandah.

buildings had to wait until 1910 before they too were lit by electricity. In the same year kitchens were improved, and a verandah was erected along the south front of the main blocks, allowing children to sit outside and soak up the sun. The buildings were also divided internally to prevent the spread of disease or fire.

Alex Skene retired in 1911 and Dr Clarkson became Medical Superintendent. His time in charge was to be one of even more dramatic change. In his first annual report in 1912 he signalled his ambition to provide life-long care in a self-contained community with farm and workshops. He saw 'a colony of children, men and women, all safe from perils that would beset them were they free, and yet all working happily together'.

The Act of 1913

When pupils were discharged at the age of eighteen they faced an often hostile world where they could be ridiculed or exploited. Many ended up in the inappropriate confines of mental hospitals. The benefits of their education were usually lost. It was a bad situation, but the Mental Deficiency and Lunacy (Scotland) Act of 1913 provided a remedy. It established in law the distinction between mental illness and mental handicap, and provided for the setting up of new institutions to accommodate the mentally handicapped. Treasury funding was made available to assist local authorities to comply. The Act also set up a new regulatory authority known as the General Board of Control to replace the Board of Lunacy. District Boards of Control were set up alongside Parish Councils who, with School Boards, had responsibility for mentally handicapped children.

The Act provided for existing establishments to become 'Certified Institutions'. Only a few met the criteria, but the Scottish National Institution was one. Local authorities could take out contracts with it, but the new law had also raised the public's expectations of assistance, and applications for admission grew. So did the paperwork, as form-filling and bureaucracy began to invade the Superintendent's time. The pressures on the Institution were increasing and in 1914, in order to free up more space, the directors decided to build a nurses' home. At the time, nursing staff were accommodated alongside the children in their dormitories, which allowed them to maintain constant supervision, but also tied them to their work and took up valuable space. The architect William J. Gibson was engaged to design the home, but before work on it could begin, the First World War broke out.

The nurses' home, officially opened in June 1925.

As the terrible conflict got bogged down in mud and trenches, the country's wealth was expended on guns and shells. The enormous drain on financial resources had a huge impact on social provision and Dr Clarkson feared that the 1913 Act was destined to become a 'dead letter' because of Government restrictions on local authority spending. Construction of the nurses' home started in July 1915, but other improvements were postponed. Work was slow, building materials were scarce and skilled men even scarcer. Costs rose and, to add to the difficulties, the weather delayed progress during the winter of 1915/16. Early in 1917 the plumber and joiner had still not finished, but by the end of the year the nurses were able to move in. It must have seemed like a different world. Instead of sleeping in the children's wards, they now had light and airy bedrooms, comfortable dining rooms, a sitting room and a reading room. There was also a recreation room with a stage for lectures, concerts and other entertainments. The space vacated in the dormitory blocks was taken up with more beds. Patient numbers rose to 500, and staff topped 100 for the first time.

While all that was going on, the Institution's name was changed. In 1916 King George V granted the honour of a royal prefix to make it the Royal Scottish National Institution (RSNI).

Financial difficulties began to ease in the early 1920s, allowing much-needed expenditure to go ahead. Land was purchased across the road from the main gate, to replace the ground taken up by the new nurses' home, and a wide-ranging programme of improvements was begun. The upheaval lasted for four years, although 1922 was singled out as 'the year of the alterations'. Children had to take up temporary residence in the covered playground while their dormitories or day rooms were renovated.

The improvements were unveiled in 1925 at a ceremony in which the Duchess of Montrose also formally opened the nurses' home.

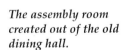

The assembly room created out of the old dining hall.

The guests inspected the work. The main dining hall had been converted into an assembly room, large enough for religious services, concerts, lectures and film shows. A new dining hall had been created out of half of the covered playground, with new kitchens and sculleries alongside. Baths, toilets and plumbing had been upgraded and new boilers installed to ensure a constant supply of hot water. The laundry had been re-equipped. The old kitchen had been converted into a workroom, the stable into a tailor's shop and a new joiner's shop had been created out of the pig sty.

Colony and Conflict

The realisation of Dr Clarkson's ambition, to provide all-life care for mentally handicapped adults, had been made possible by the 1913 Act, but thwarted by the war. Priority had to be given to upgrading the Institution after the war, but now, with that done, the way was clear to start looking for a site for an industrial colony. The neighbouring Glenbervie Estate came on the market in 1924, but the Carron Company believed it contained workable coal and outbid the Institution. It was a short-lived disappointment: the following year the directors were able to buy the nearby Larbert

Larbert Estate – 750 acres of space and seclusion for the new industrial colony.

Larbert House was built in the 1820s to the designs of David Hamilton, although the square tower over the entrance was added in the late nineteenth century.

The appeal for funds was pursued with energy.

£70,000 APPEAL.

New Colony for Mental Defectives at Larbert.

LIFE SUPERVISION.

An appeal is being made for £70,000 to es[tablish] a new colony for whole-life care in connectio[n with] the Royal Scottish National Institution, [for] for the Maintenance and Training of [Mental] Defective Children.

A meeting convened at the instance of [the Insti]tution was held in the City Chambers, [this afternoon for the purpose of de[...] ... home, for which the adjac[ent]

THE ROYAL SCOTTISH NATIONAL INSTITUTION, LARBERT.

COLONY.

[At the instanc]e of the DIRECTORS of THE ROYAL [NA]TIONAL INSTITUTION, LARBERT, [for the Maintena]nce and Training of Mental Defec[tives ... are Conven]ing a PUBLIC MEET[ING] [to be held in the BANQUET]ING HALL, [...CHAMBERS, GLASGOW, on the ...] [THU]RSDAY, 28th APRIL, at Half-[...] [...SCHE]ME for Whole-Life Care, initiated [...] the ..., Institution for [...]

£70,000 NEEDED

To Establish Mental Institution at Larbert

Sir Alexander Gracie, chairman of the Royal Scottish National Institution for Mental Defectives, Larbert, at the annual meeting of the Institution in Glasgow yesterday, made an earnest appeal for increased financial assistance.

Larbert Estate, which adjoined the Institution, he said, had been purchased for the purpose of establishing a colony for the training of adult defectives.

The sum of £70,000 was required within the next two years to complete the buildings and equipment necessary for 300 patients. That was in addition to the sum of [...] £13,000, which h[...]

[...]ed in 186[...] [...] is licen[...] [...] long ha[...] [...] list. E[...] [...] where [...] knitting, [...]iloring, [...]o the [...]ars, both [...]oved n[...] [...]d contr[...] [...]r long [...] s only [...]uitable [...]eful o[...] NAT[...]

THE ROYAL SCOTTISH NAT[IONAL] INSTITUTION, LARBERT.

COLONY.

AT THE INSTANCE of the DIRECTORS of [the] SCOTTISH NATIONAL INSTITUTION, LAR[BERT, for] the Maintenance and Training of Mental [Defectives] HAVE PLEASURE IN CONVENING a PUB[LIC MEET]ING of the CITIZENS to be HELD in [the CITY] CHAMBERS, EDINBURGH, on the AFT[ERNOON of] TUESDAY, 3rd May, at Three o'clock, for th[e] hearing of the NEW COLONY SCHEME f[or Whole-Life] Care initiated in connection with the Instituti[on, for which] the adjacent Larbert Estate has been acqui[red.]

The MEETING will be Addressed by the [...] EARL OF MAR AND KELLIE, K.T.; the R[ight Hon. Lord] POLWARTH, C.B.E.; the Right Hon. L[...] C.M.G., and others.

All interested are cordially inv[ited.]

ALEX. STEVENSON, [...]

City Chambers, Edinburgh,
26th April, 1927.

£70,000 APPEAL

Sir John Gilmour's Support for Mental Defective Project

NEW PERMANENT HOME

An appeal for £70,000—for the establishment of the first colony in Scotland where life-care can be given to mental defectives, who at present must be discharged from the Royal Scottish National Institution for Mental Defectives at Larbert on attaining the age of 21—was formally brought before the citizens of Glasgow and of Scotland generally at a meeting in Glasgow yesterday convened by Lord Provost Mason.

The directors of the Institution have already purchased Larbert Estate, which adjoins the Institution, and the money appealed for is necessary for the completion of the buildings and equipment of the new colony, which will accommodate over 300 patients.

"Permanent Care" Not Permanent

The Secretary of State for Scotland, Sir John Gilmour, Bt., who was one of the principal speakers at the meeting, promised his sympathetic support of the new scheme both in his official and his private capacity. It was, he said, often the earnest and natural desire of the parent to get a child back from the Institution where it had improved mentally and physically, but unless that carried with it the fact that the unfortunates were going to be still supervised and cared for all the good work of the training was lost, and the last state of the unfortunate was worse than the first.

Sometimes they used the words "permanent care" mistakenly, and he wanted to emphasise that every one of these cases was reviewed either within a year or two years.

336 New Patients

Sir Alexander Gracie, chairman of the Institution directors, pointed out that the Institution had been in existence for about 65 years, and the buildings were now licensed to accommodate 500 pupils. The mansion-house on Larbert Estate was being altered for the new scheme to accommodate about 36 patients, and it was the intention to build six cottages—each to accommodate about 50 patients—and to build and equip workshops.

Colonies had been in existence in England, America, and all over Europe for many years, but nothing of the sort had been done in Scotland.

Th[e] other speakers included the Lord Provost, who presided; Principal Sir Donald MacAlister, of Glasgow University; and Sir Frederick Gardiner.

House and its 750 acre estate – the property of the Institution's former President, the late Sir John H. N. Graham. It cost £40,000, and to pay for it some invested securities had to be realised, but money came from other sources too. The mother of a child at the Institution donated £1000 (about £34,000 in today's money) and the Women's Citizens' Association of Scotland contributed £10,000 which they later increased to £12,000.

Plans were drawn up for a colony where 300 people would be able to work on the land, or at various occupations, to meet the needs of the establishment, and perhaps make a small profit. The main buildings were arranged in a shallow crescent with a central administration block and nurses' home, and five villas, each designed to house 50 patients. The three to the east were intended for male residents and the two to the west for females. A hospital and two villas for less able patients were also planned along with workshops, services and recreation facilities. The estimated cost was £70,000 and an appeal was launched to raise the money. Public meetings were held in Glasgow and Edinburgh chaired by the respective Lord Provosts, and a garden party was held at Larbert House in July 1927. Rain fell so heavily that the attendance was reduced from an expected 2000 to only 300, but Sir Alexander Gracie, chairman of the Board of Directors, persevered. He held a meeting in the house at which he, Dr Clarkson, and the appeal director Henry Crowe, extolled the need for the Colony. Sir Donald

Foundations for the administration block.

MacAllister, principal of Glasgow University and a supporter of the Institution, broadcast an appeal on the BBC, and a cheque for £1,000 arrived two days later. Other donations followed.

While fund-raising for the new buildings gathered pace, a group of private residents were settling into Larbert House. The magnificent old mansion, with its carved fireplaces and elegant interiors, had been adapted to accommodate 36 private patients paying the full cost of their maintenance. They were the first people over twenty-one years of age to be admitted to the Institution. The house was opened in July 1927.

The following year sufficient funds were in place to start building the villas. A space was left between them for the administration block which was begun two years later. Everything was ready by May 1933 for 50 boys to walk from the old Institution to take up residence. They were followed in July by 50 girls. In March 1934 another 50 boys moved in and, as space was vacated in what became known as the 'juvenile site', it was quickly filled by new arrivals. Soon, over 700 children, teenagers and young adults were staying at the two sites.

The Colony was officially opened by the Countess of Mar and Kellie on 12th September 1935. After the speeches, the Bonnybridge and District Silver Band played popular music while the directors and guests took tea in a large marquee. They later toured the buildings and saw a display of work.

Construction of the administration block, between the villas.

The Colony from the west.

The opening also marked a change at the top. Dr Clarkson, who had seen his vision of the Colony realised, retired on 30th September. His successor was Dr Thomas Spence whose time in charge was to prove every bit as dramatic.

With the Colony open, the directors turned their attention again to the juvenile site. There the three-storied accommodation blocks had reached an age when they were no longer suited for their purpose, and unable to be adapted to modern needs. The directors wanted to replace them with seven home-like villas: three for girls and four for boys. Each villa would be self contained and have 50 beds. A nursing villa for 60 mentally and physically handicapped children was also proposed, and an appeal for funds was launched. But it was 1939, and once again a world war stopped development.

There were immediate staffing problems as men were called-up into the services and nurses resigned to take higher paid, more glamorous, jobs in emergency hospitals, or munitions factories. Fewer, less experienced, staff were left to cope with patient numbers that rose to over 900 in 1940 when 130 'difficult' adult male patients were transferred from Gogarburn Hospital, where their accommodation had been taken over as an emergency hospital. They were expected to be at the Colony for only a few months, but remained until 1943. They levelled ground in front of the villas for a football field, but their presence placed a heavy burden on a short-staffed voluntary institution.

From left to right: *Dr Edith Chalmers, who started as Assistant Medical Officer in 1933 and retired, effectively as deputy Superintendent, in 1956; Miss Robertson who became Deputy Matron; unknown; Dr Spence, who retired in 1954; Miss Cummings – the picture is thought to show her retiral as Matron in October 1953; and Miss Tait, who succeeded her.*

Into the NHS

After the war the buildings looked shabby and everything was in short supply, especially bed linen, but there were more pressing realities to face up to. Dunipace Estate was purchased in 1945 to meet an urgent need for more beds for mentally handicapped people, but plans to develop it, or expand the Colony, were stopped by proposals for a new trunk road. It was intended as a link between Glasgow and the Kincardine Bridge, and the route ran diagonally across Larbert and Dunipace Estates. The road plans threatened the working of the two estates, but a bigger threat, to the existence of the charity itself, came with the National Health Service (Scotland) Act. People who believed in the Institution's voluntary character had deep reservations about the proposals, but the idea of state health provision was unstoppable, and the Act became law in 1948. The RSNI became a 'special hospital' under the Western Regional Hospital Board and the 'most excellent charity' ceased to exist. The funds, endowments, 1600 acres of ground, and buildings with a capacity for nearly 800 residents, were transferred to the state.

The new NHS also inherited a tricky problem. The Board of Control had been arguing for some time that there was a big shortage of beds for mentally handicapped people. The upheavals of the late 1940s had prevented the RSNI from doing anything about it, but the legal responsibility lay with the local authorities. A few had provided accommodation, but most had chosen to meet their obligations by paying for space at the RSNI. The arrangement had

New nursing pavilion at the juvenile site – staff also called the juvenile site the 'Tute', short for Institution.

met their immediate needs, but the country was left with an inadequate level of provision at a time when the economy was struggling to recover from the war.

A Board of Management, answerable to the Western Regional Hospital Board, had charge of the Institution's affairs, but for a few years its actions were restricted to cautious husbandry of scarce funds. Some progress was made. The Colony's hospital was converted into a 56-bed villa and a staff bicycle shed was built. Shops, fitted-up by in-house staff, were opened at both sites and filled an important need for patients, relatives and staff. More land was purchased to expand the juvenile site and a new nursing pavilion for 60 children with multiple handicaps was planned, but in September 1954, before it was built, Dr Spence resigned; he was succeeded by Dr J. B. Methven. The new pavilion was opened in 1956, although its occupancy was delayed due to staff shortages and an outbreak of dysentery.

The economic situation began to improve through the 1950s, but instead of building up facilities in those parts of the country where there were none, the NHS chose to expand at Larbert. A twelve-year plan, to increase bed numbers to over 1300 at a cost of £1 million, was set up in 1956. The old blocks, which the directors had wanted to replace in 1939, were kept in use, because any new buildings had to add to, not replace, existing accommodation. The first phase, which included developments on both sites, was completed in 1959. At the same time, space standards were revised allowing 50-bed villas to hold between 58 and 62 people.

The twelve-year plan was substantially completed by 1967 when Arthur Woodburn, MP for Clackmannan and East Stirling, opened a new nursing pavilion and two villas at the juvenile site. During this time the Mental Welfare Commission replaced the Board of Control, as one of the measures in the Mental Health (Scotland) Act of 1960.

The Institution celebrated its centenary in May 1963. A special lunch was held at the Colony: guest of honour was Sir James

Younger, Lord Lieutenant of Clackmannan. He paid tribute to the pioneers whose foresight had led to the Institution being established, and unveiled a plaque to mark the opening of the new Treatment Unit. After the ceremony the guests inspected the unit and also viewed one of the new single-storey nursing pavilions (later named Lorne/Dornoch and Moray/Beauly), and one of the unfinished two-storey villas (Morar and Solway).

The visitors were no doubt impressed by the obvious progress, but it was not just the buildings that had changed. Admission criteria had shifted from educational to clinical need and many of the patients were more handicapped than those taken in by the pre-NHS Institution. The dormitories were crowded, and toilet and washing facilities were inadequate to deal with the increased numbers. The staff-to-patient ratio was low and staff retention, training and recruitment were difficult. So it was a different Institution that Dr David Primrose inherited in 1967 when he became the last Physician Superintendent – the title was dropped when he retired in 1985. He wrote and lectured widely on the causes of mental handicap, and his research into these earned him the Burden Medal and prize.

Accommodation was upgraded as funds became available and reallocated where appropriate; some older male patients, who had difficulty with stairs, were moved to ground level from second-floor dormitories. Occupational therapy buildings were erected on both sites and two therapists were appointed. Two new Consultant posts were created, allowing outpatients' clinics to be started in Dumbarton and Ayr; there were other clinics at Falkirk and Stirling. A chiropodist, a dentist and assistant, and additional physiotherapy staff were also appointed.

In the early 1970s the 'Institution' became a 'Hospital' and ward numbers were replaced by names; lochs and rivers for the Colony site, and islands for the juvenile site. The Forth Valley Health Board took over from the Western Regional Hospital Board in April 1974.

Villa (Solway) completed about 1963.

A day room in Skye, one of the 'Merchiston' units completed in 1983. Day rooms at RSNH were also known as 'parlours'.

Dormitory in Beauly about 1983.

Change, Renewal and Trust Status

Patient numbers remained constant at 1325 into the 1980s, but the idea of moving from institutional to community care was gaining ground. Its basis was that people should be in the community if a better quality of life and care was available there, and only those with a clinical need should be in hospital. The discharge of more able patients into self-tenancies and supervised, and supported accommodation, gathered pace, aided by a social work service established at the hospital in 1981 by Central Regional Council. Admissions of children slowed, and then stopped, as community paediatric and nursing services were developed.

The old juvenile blocks, which the directors had wanted to replace in 1939, were finally vacated in 1983 when four new wards, named Nevis, Pentland, Rannoch and Skye were opened on the Colony site. They were built to a design developed at Merchiston Hospital and later became mixed-sex wards – a departure from previous practice of segregating male and female residents.

Despite some reduction in bed numbers, staffing levels were still low when a critical Mental Welfare Commission report became the catalyst for a television documentary in the 'World in Action' series. It was transmitted in June 1986 under the title 'Without Due Care' and its criticisms of the RSNH and Lennox Castle Hospital caused an outcry. The local MP, Denis Canavan, demanded an enquiry, and Forth Valley Health Board shouted foul. They had already made changes and approved substantial funding: by the end of 1985 three bungalows had been opened and the development of the thirty-bed 'Inver' unit and hydrotherapy pool was under way. Staff morale suffered, but the hospital's work went

The first three 'kit house' bungalows were erected by a local builder and used to help patients adapt to life in the community.

The hydrotherapy pool.

The Snoezelen room, set up in the Lorne/ Dornoch building in 1991, was paid for by a generous donation.

Inver unit.

on. The culture began to change, more attention was given to patients' social needs, and when the national media had lost interest, the Falkirk Herald put the record straight with a series of positive articles.

The pace of change quickened through the late 1980s when the Mental Handicap Services Unit was set up under General Manager, Derek Pollacchi. Staffing levels improved, as did morale and conditions. A staff newsletter, Christmas cards printed from residents' artwork and award-winning educational videos were produced. Health Boards in other areas were given greater encouragement to take their patients back and the drive to reduce numbers was stepped up. Existing accommodation was upgraded and new facilities were opened, including community homes in Stirling, Falkirk and Dunblane, a new boiler house, five new bungalows, and the 'state-of-the-art' Ochil Park development.

Many of the developments were made possible by the Board's approval of a five-year plan (it was completed in four) to concentrate the hospital on the Colony site and to pay for it by disposing of the juvenile site. Through the late 1980s the patients from its remaining wards were 'resettled' – although the process was inevitably unsettling for them – and the site was vacated at the end of 1991.

The final move coincided with the commissioning of Ochil Park. Its design was developed by RSNH managers and was as innovatory as the original Institution buildings. It consisted of six, ten-bedded, linked bungalows for highly dependent patients and was officially opened in September 1992 by Lord Fraser of Carmyllie, Minister of State at the Scottish Office. The bed complement had now been reduced to 600 and, as if to emphasise the changing times, Ard and Brora, the two original Colony villas adjacent to Ochil Park, were demolished within months of its opening.

Ochil Park.

Theresa Stewart, a patient, celebrated her 100th birthday in August 1993 by opening the Ochil Park Landscape Garden.

Ochil Park.

Community House in Brightons.

Trust Headquarters was set up in the Colony's old administrative block.

Therapy Garden

Community House in Falkirk.

The physical developments were paralleled by staff changes. The nurse-to-patient ratio dramatically improved, a community nursing department was developed and significant improvements were made in the numbers of allied professions. Most of these were based at a Clinical Services Centre, set up in 1993 in the building which had opened thirty years earlier as the Treatment Unit.

The management team courted controversy when the government published its white paper for the National Health Service and Community Care Act of 1990. They proposed a pilot scheme to make the hospital self-governing, but the move was opposed by staff in a union ballot, and condemned by civil servants, the local MP and other politicians. But Forth Valley Health Board supported it, and in 1993 the hospital became one of the first in Scotland to acquire Trust status. Its new title was the Royal Scottish National Hospital and Community NHS Trust.

The Trust's first year was also its last. As other hospitals in the Forth Valley area responded to the new legislation and formed trusts, it became clear that community and mental health services would be the only areas left under direct Health Board control. The RSNH trust took the initiative and proposed a new trust incorporating Bellsdyke Hospital and the other services. The enlarged Central Scotland Healthcare NHS Trust came into being in 1994. After further Health Service restructuring in the late 1990s it was expanded to include GPs and other primary care services and renamed Forth Valley Primary Care NHS Trust.

The reduction in patient numbers has continued throughout this period of change until, in the first year of the new millennium, there are a thousand fewer beds in the hospital than in the peak years of the 1960s and 70s. The fall in numbers is expected to go on until only a few people remain in Health Service care. When that happens, the Royal Scottish National Hospital is scheduled to close, 140 years after it first opened its doors to give mentally handicapped children a chance of fulfilment. The challenge for twenty-first century society will be to allow the large institutions to fade into history and foster the development of such children's lives in homely domestic settings.

Schoolrooms

Education was a primary purpose of the original Institution, but to begin with there was only one schoolroom. It was soon outgrown by the numbers of children and, for a time, classes had to be staggered. Two small rooms were also made available for infants. 'Larger and more commodious' schoolrooms, with accommodation for over 100 children, were provided as part of the building extensions of the 1870s. They were fitted out with tiered floors and rows of long desks, with narrow forms for children to sit on. Separate rooms were provided for the private, fee-paying, children.

A fourth schoolroom was completed in 1884 and the old laundry was converted into new classrooms about ten years later. Lessons were timetabled in periods which started with prayers and praise at 10.00 a.m. and finished, after singing, at 4.30 p.m. Between those times, academic subjects and craft skills had been taught, along with drill, objects and money. There was also a twice-weekly evening dancing class in the winter months.

In 1912 the house joiner, assisted by some of the boys, levelled the 1870s classroom floors, introduced roof lights and improved the ventilation. They also cut the long desks into smaller ones for two children. The rooms could have been in any school, as could practices like holding an annual prize-day to reward achievement, but there were important differences too. Children spent half a day at school and half at occupational training. Those who were unlikely to benefit from scholastic education stayed in the day rooms, where nurses taught them habits of cleanliness, decency and simple housework. Children were still grouped in occupational and educable classes and taught a similar curriculum up to the 1980s, when the last child in the hospital reached the upper legal age limit.

Important elements of schooling included the clock and the shop – the glass-fronted cupboard behind the nurses. The 'shop lesson' was introduced in 1869 to help children identify coins and learn the use of scales, weights and money. The picture was taken after 1912 because the raked line of the old tiered seating can be seen to the left of the shop.

Play was also regarded as an important element of a child's life, although some had to be taught how to play. Children with a low mental age went to kindergarten classes and, when profoundly handicapped children were taken in under the NHS, attempts were made to provide a learning experience for them. These used home-grown ideas of sensory stimulation similar to those incorporated in later 'Snoezelen' rooms.

A boys' class in the 1930s.

Kindergarten class.

A 1970s classroom.

Occupations

Much of the 'education' at the early Institution was aimed at teaching children tasks which might help them find employment when they were discharged. Girls assisted in the laundry and kitchen. They received instruction in the making or repairing of

Girls learning housekeeping skills.

clothing and in general housework skills like dressing, bed making, sweeping, cleaning and polishing. They also learned needlework skills: hemming, knitting, embroidery and crochet work. Younger boys made brushes, mats and rugs, while the older boys did joinery, tailoring and mending, cobbling or gardening. One boy became such an expert with a stocking machine that he outstripped demand for stockings and socks for the whole Institution. Boys also assisted the engineer and tradesmen. Others were trusted to go to the railway station as messengers, or collect the post and the morning newspapers. The tailor and sewing maid supervised the making of staff uniforms, and the children also made up bedding from bolts of linen or woollen cloth, including all the sheets and blankets for the new Colony.

Some discharged children did find gainful employment, albeit in places where guidance was on hand. Boys worked as tailors or cabinet-makers, while girls often found work as domestic servants. Some girls, thought likely to be at risk in the outside world, stayed on at the Institution as maids. Children were sometimes 'boarded out', often on farms, with families who they worked for. Others were sent home early, on probationary discharge, and if reports on conduct and work were satisfactory they were formally discharged.

Girls' sewing lesson.

Boys learning rug-making; a caged bird, on the right, keeps them company.

Some former pupils, in employment, returned to the Institution for a holiday.

Colony residents were not originally expected to be discharged, so employment there had to be constant. The women were given similar tasks to the girls at the Institution, while a small group tended the poultry farm. Men undertook more strenuous labour on the farm, or in the gardens, or workshops. Some also worked in the boiler house, on lorries, or with the plumber and painters. Most of these activities continued under the NHS.

The occupational therapist posts of the late 1960s were absorbed into the nursing structure in the early 1970s, and so it was nursing staff who supervised the work therapies of the time. Tasks included packaging small goods, stripping old telephones to recover valuable parts, or making concrete slabs. Other patients worked in industries outside the hospital where they learned community skills, as well as earning some money! They were accommodated in the old male staff hostel, later known as Morven.

Occupational therapists were reintroduced in the mid-1980s. Their first base was at the juvenile site, but after about a year, the growing department moved to the old sewing room and the two original occupational or work therapy sheds on the Colony site. These were equipped to help stimulate the patients and develop their community skills. The therapy garden and woodland walk were set up alongside in the early 1990s to provide a place for people to work in, but also one to relax in and enjoy. As the most able people moved into the community, the therapists adapted their programmes to meet the more demanding needs of those who remained in hospital.

ARTICLES MADE BY THE CHILDREN.

MADE.

37 Bed Binders.
90 Bed Mats.
332 Sheets.
176 Pillow Cases.
136 Bath Rollers and Towels.
59 Table Cloths.
356 Table Napkins.
32 pairs Curtains.
381 Pinafores.
429 Night Dresses.
91 Chemises.
60 Petticoats.
78 Semmits.
178 pairs Knickers.
27 „ Combinations.
43 „ Pants.
12 Camisoles.
14 Bed Jackets.
8 Wrappers.
39 Dresses.
21 Blouses.
5 Skirts.
5 Aprons.
119 Squares.
12 Tea Bags.
4 Work Bags.
31 Night Dress Bags.
4 Sewing Sets.
52 Coat Hangers.
6 pair Boot Trees.
20 Suede Leather Bags.
74 Rugs.
41 Door Mats.
5 Work Stands.
50 Beaded Mats.
6 Hearth Brushes.

CROCHETED.

2 pairs D'Oyleys.
10½ „ Towel Ends.
397 Milk Jug Covers.

WOVEN.

57 Ties.
5 Hand Loom Towels.

RAFFIA AND CANE WORK.

11 Sets Raffia Dinner Mats.
207 Raffia Bags.
6 Raffia Hats.
12 Cane Trays.
26 Cane Work Baskets.
6 Raffia Work Baskets.

KNITTED.

869 pairs Stockings.
23 „ „ re-footed.
11 „ Bed Socks.
17 „ Bedroom Slippers.
72 Bed Jackets.
10 Scarves.
46 Semmits.
21 Baby's Jackets.
10 pairs Baby's Knickers.
5 Baby's Caps.
4 Jumpers.
1 Dress.
5 pairs Mittens.
2 „ Knee Caps.
2 Egg Coseys.
4 Hot-Water Bag Covers.

EMBROIDERED.

82 Tray Cloths.
82 Cushion Covers.
19 Chair Back Covers.
10 Piano Top Covers.
8 Sideboard Covers.
76 Tea Cosy Covers.
57 Table Centres.
5 Table Covers.
5 Table Scarves.
38 Dinner Mats.
3 Breakfast Sets.
13 Supper Cloths.
8 Duchesse Sets.
48 Brush and Comb Bags.
4 Pyjama Cases.
9 Linen Bags.
12 Crochet Bags.
5 Sponge Bags.
24 Bags, assorted.
75 Toilet Cases.
4 Needle Books.
2 Blotters.
19 Lavender Bags.
107 Odd Mats.
3 Canvas Runners.
22 Handkerchief Cases.
34 Feeders.

BARBOLA WORK.

29 Bowls.
32 Trays.
55 Boxes.
12 Candle Sticks.

LACQUERED WORK.

10 Boxes.
2 Mirrors.

1925 directors' report.

Tailoring at the Colony.

The Colony joinery workshop.

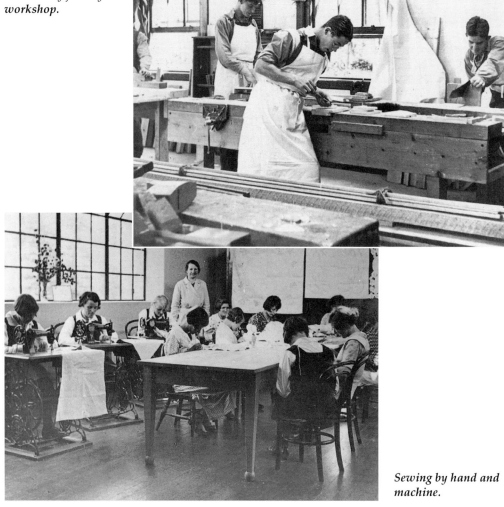

Sewing by hand and machine.

Morven was used as a hostel, from about 1970, to prepare male patients for a move into the community.

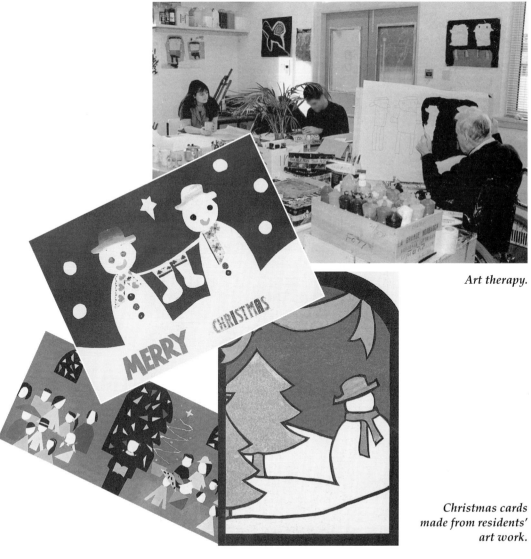

Art therapy.

Christmas cards made from residents' art work.

An array of goods on offer at a sale of work.

*A wide range of
needlework skills
produced this display
of articles for sale.*

Sales of Work

A sale of work in 1912 was described as a 'new development'. It earned over £45 and the next year's sale raised over £100, but during the war years which followed receipts dropped. They started to recover in the early 1920s when an annual, two-day, pre-Christmas sale of work was started and other sales of work were held at a variety of functions. Dr Clarkson set up a special, self-perpetuating fund for training children in arts and crafts, and when the results were sold, the proceeds were put back into the fund to purchase new materials. Articles made by the boys included rugs, baskets, stockings, scarves, cosies, leather goods, cushions and fender stools. Girls made bed spreads, cuffs, cravats, antimacassars, and the more prosaic sheets, towels, dusters, aprons, underwear and handkerchiefs. Raffia work by younger children was sold alongside marquetry, china painting and artificial flowers made from fish scales and shells! Pot plants and flowers from the garden always found a ready sale. Work also won prizes at local exhibitions.

Craft items including a model locomotive.

Toys for Christmas.

The Sanatorium; the verandah was later extended and enclosed.

Nursing villas at the Colony.

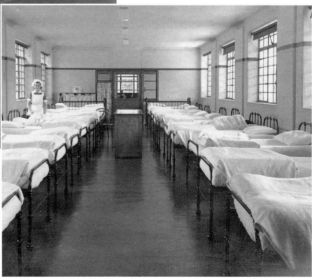

Nursing villa dormitory.

Hospitals

The Institution was not a hospital, although children inevitably became ill and needed medical treatment. General hospitals were neither equipped, nor willing, to accept people with mental problems and so the Institution provided its own hospital facilities.

The first 'sick wards' were located in the main building. They provided a place to nurse children, but were of little help in preventing the spread of disease. The task of isolating illnesses like scarlet fever, chicken pox, measles, whooping cough and gastric fever was almost constant. A scarlet fever outbreak in 1883 was typical of the risks faced by the Institution. A girl, who spent the school holiday in Glasgow with her family, was found to be infected the day after she returned. The disease spread to 34 other children, two of whom died. It could not be checked because a 26-bed hospital, set up in 1873, was occupied by children needing medical care.

Another building was clearly needed, and so a new infectious diseases 'cottage hospital', with accommodation for up to fourteen children and their nurses, was erected in 1885/86. It quickly proved its worth by helping to contain another outbreak of scarlet fever. The Institution also kept infectious diseases at bay by using carbolic soaps and sticking to 'antiseptic principles'.

As the numbers of children increased, so did the outbreaks of disease and by the mid-1890s the cottage hospital was struggling to cope. Work started on building the new 'sanatorium' in 1903. It was completed in 1905. It had a large day room, two eight-bedded wards and two small wards with two beds each. There was also a dispensary, operating room, bathrooms and kitchen. Accommodation for nursing staff was provided above the day room. Fresh air was believed to be an essential element in treating a variety of infections, and so a verandah and large steel casement windows were provided to give the children as much air as possible. Care was also taken to circulate air through inlets and natural exhaust ventilators, and there were no square corners where dust and germs could gather.

An unfortunate echo of the 1883 scarlet fever outbreak occurred in 1937. The family of a boy who returned from the Christmas holiday failed to tell staff that measles was present at home and a severe epidemic followed. It was made worse because the Institution had been free of the disease for nine years, and compounded by a flu epidemic affecting the staff.

A hospital and two nursing villas for severely handicapped people were completed at the Colony in 1937. The villas had dormitories, single rooms, dining rooms and day rooms. They also had large windows and verandahs to provide fresh air and daylight. The hospital had similar accommodation, but was also equipped with a laboratory, surgery, dental room, dispensary and waiting room. The central section of the building had an upper floor of five rooms. They opened onto balconies so that tuberculosis sufferers could be wheeled out into clean, fresh air in all seasons!

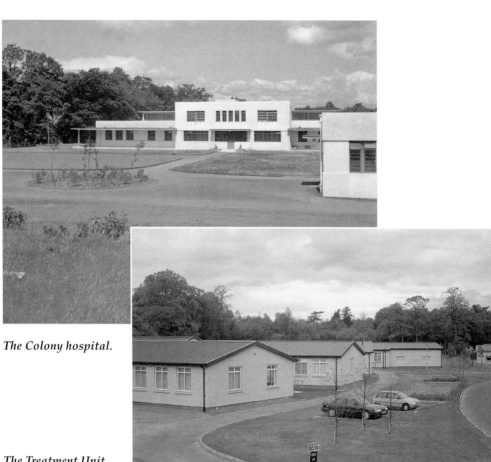

The Colony hospital.

The Treatment Unit, opened in 1963.

The hospital was used for its designed purpose for only a few years. During the Second World War it was occupied by the overspill patients from Gogarburn Hospital, but when they moved out, staff shortages prevented it from being used as a hospital again. It was put to various uses until the early 1950s when it was converted into a villa. It was called Lomond when the wards were given names, and the nursing villas became Garry and Fyne.

The opening of the Treatment Unit in 1963 continued on-site provision of medical and isolation hospital facilities. It had wards for patients with tuberculosis, infectious diseases, or acute mental and physical disabilities. There was a physiotherapy department equipped with a hoist that could be swung over the side of a deep bath and lowered to allow patients to exercise in the water. The unit also had staff-rooms, store rooms, X-ray, minor theatre, dental and sterilising departments, pharmacy and dark room, and an out-patient department with diagnostic and treatment facilities.

General medical care for residents was increasingly carried out, from the 1960s, by local general practitioners. They provided daily visits to wards and were on call for emergencies, complementing the psychiatric care given by the hospital's own specialist medical staff.

Staff Housing

The Institution was conceived as a home, a self-contained community where staff and children lived together in the same buildings. The idea of having separate accommodation for staff only started to take hold in the late nineteenth century. The lodge-house at the main entrance was completed in 1887. It was intended to give the Institution more security and privacy, but it also provided a house. A married man, his family, and two governesses, squeezed into it first, and it was later occupied by the engineer and his family. When it ceased to be a staff residence it was adapted for use by young female patients.

The Park, a two-storey house with a private tennis court, was built in 1896 for the Superintendent. It allowed the space he had occupied in the main building to be converted into accommodation for fee-paying children. When the Colony was built, a house was

John Buick was a gardener; here Mrs Buick and son Billy feed the chickens outside their house in Garden Square.

provided there for the Superintendent. It was called Westerpark, borrowing the 'Park' name from the east, or easter, site. The Park was converted into a villa for private, fee-paying, girls, and after Westerpark ceased to be a staff residence, it was used as a pre-discharge training unit for female patients. (It is not known if the 'Park' name was originally derived from Dr Brodie's house at Colinton which was known as Hope Park.)

The provision of staff houses became more of a priority in the twentieth century. Unmarried male staff were not employed 'for obvious reasons', but suitable married men were difficult to recruit because there was no suitable housing. Cottages for the joiner and gardener were completed in 1905, and the old isolation hospital at the Institution was converted into staff quarters in 1936. At the same time, new houses were built opposite the Institution site and at the Colony along the Old Denny Road. A number of houses and gate lodges on Larbert Estate were made available to staff including four that formed part of a courtyard known as Garden Square. It sat between the walled garden and Westerpark. The acquisition of Dunipace Estate provided more cottages for staff working on the land. A house called Torwoodlea, across the road from the Institution, was acquired in 1938 for the Senior Medical Officer. Eight new houses were built in 1956 in Graham Avenue and others followed in the early 1960s. Many had been sold to sitting tenants by the 1990s.

The covered playground.

Covered Playground

The need for a covered playground, or recreation hall, was recognised in the 1860s, but it was not until the end of the century that sufficient funds, helped by a donation of £1000, became available. The official opening was held in June 1900 and special trains were laid on from Glasgow and Edinburgh to bring guests to Larbert. The ceremony was performed by Lady Overtoun. She used a silver key, presented to her by the architects and contractors, to open the door and allow the assembled company to enter the building. It had been designed by Falkirk architect William Black, with consultant architect Sydney Mitchell of Edinburgh advising on the large unbroken roof span. The roof was supported by steel lattice girders resting on iron columns. They were built into the walls, so as not to obstruct the 165 feet long by 60 feet wide floor space. The floor was of pitch-pine blocks, laid on a bed of concrete. The walls were of roughcast brick with stone facings on the outside and tiles to a height of 4 feet 6 inches inside. Windows in the walls, and dormer windows in the roof, provided daylight.

On cold, wet days, before the covered playground was built, children had to be kept amused in their day rooms, as here, with swings rigged from hooks in the ceiling.

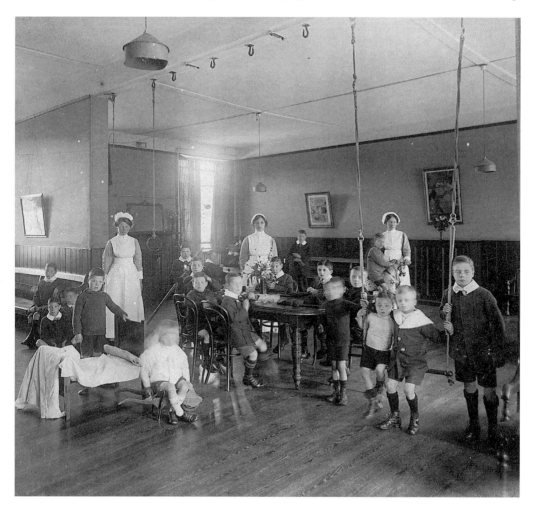

Gymnastic display.

The building cost more than the budget figure and it was opened with a deficit of £190, but Lord Overtoun challenged the assembled company to donate £90 and he would contribute the balance of £100. The gentlemen on the platform more than met his challenge and the debt was cleared. One of the girls presented Lady Overtoun with a bouquet of flowers and the guests were entertained outside by the Carron Ironworks Band.

The covered playground was reduced in size in the 1920s when part of it was taken over as the dining hall.

The New Block

New accommodation for fifty additional pupils was opened in July 1907 by Lady Graham of Larbert House, wife of the Society's president, Sir John H. N. Graham. The two-storey block occupied a site between the main building and the railway. On the ground floor there were well-furnished day rooms, a ten-bedded dormitory, two small bedrooms, a dining hall with small kitchen, baths, toilets, cloakroom and waiting room. On the upper floor were four ten-bedded dormitories and rooms for the head attendant. All rooms had electric lighting, open fireplaces and hot water radiators.

The architects, A & W Black of Falkirk, presented Lady Graham with a gold key for the ceremonial opening and to keep as a souvenir. After her speech, and various votes of thanks, the company adjourned for tea. Musical entertainment was provided in the grounds by the Wright Memorial Brass Band from Camelon.

The new block, opened in 1907.

A day room in the new block.

Water and Drainage

There was no civic drainage or water supply when the first buildings were erected and so a well was sunk. Some of the stronger boys had the task of pumping water from it into a storage tank. Pipes were laid to connect the tank to buildings. Rain water was also collected in cisterns, for washing purposes.

Access to a spring on Torwood Estate was granted in 1865, but it was not tapped until 1870 delaying the use of new kitchens installed the previous year. The water was hard and although it was good for cooking and drinking, rain water was still used for washing. A water supply from Falkirk Water Trust was connected in the 1890s.

Drains were initially led into cesspools, but sewage filtration tanks were erected in 1888 to reduce the amount of pollution going into the neighbouring burn. When the Institution was connected into the new District Drainage System in 1894 the old tanks were roofed and turned into chicken houses.

Building the Colony boiler house.

Heating

One of the problems which the modifications of the 1860s and 70s sought to improve was the difficulty of heating the stone buildings, with their high ceilings and large windows. Heating pipes had been led throughout the buildings by 1876 and the open fires, which were regarded as dangerous by some staff, were disused. But their cheerfulness was soon missed and they were quickly reinstated.

New, more efficient, boilers were installed in the early 1920s. They saved 300 tons of coal a year while producing an ample supply of steam for heating. They also put an end to the thick black smoke that used to pour from the old chimney, although construction of the new chimney was marred by a fatal accident to one of the men working on it.

The Colony's boilers provided hot water for radiators, domestic use, kitchen and laundry. They were upgraded in the 1960s, but the days of coal-burning were well and truly over when a new boiler house was commissioned in 1990. It was designed to burn either oil or gas, to ensure uninterrupted operation.

New boiler house, 1990.

Dining room for private, fee-paying, children.

Kitchens and Dining Halls

Dr Brodie's ideal of having self-contained accommodation blocks with their own catering arrangements was eventually abandoned by the directors, and a communal dining hall and kitchen were set up. Separate dining rooms were, however, retained for the fee-paying children.

The furnishings of the early kitchen were apparently 'never suitable' and so, in the 1890s, it was re-equipped. At the same time the 'uneven' floor was re-laid with 'plain but cheerfully patterned' tiles and a dado of white tiles was applied to the walls. The dining hall was also enlarged, redecorated and refurnished to accommodate over 160 children.

The re-equipped kitchen of the 1890s with its 'plain but cheerfully patterned' tiled floor.

The new kitchen in the 1920s.

*The Colony kitchen
soon after
installation.*

*The dining hall,
opened in 1925 in
part of the covered
playground.*

In the 1920s part of the covered playground was converted into a dining hall. It seated 340 children, with eight or ten at each table. A new kitchen, with new equipment, was built next to it. Between kitchen and dining hall was a steam-heated service table which kept food hot until it was served. Food for the nurses' home, and the private children's dining hall, was taken in trolleys and kept hot in service tables until it was required. The kitchens on both sites were upgraded again many times, and in the 1970s wards were also equipped with their own small kitchens and dining facilities.

Laundry

The Institution opened with no laundry facilities, which must have caused a few problems. To solve them a forty-foot-square temporary building, made of wood with brick partitions, was quickly erected. It contained a coal-house and stable, as well as the laundry and wash-house, but within months of being opened, it was destroyed by fire. Laundry had to be sent to the Magdalene Home in Maryhill, Glasgow, until new facilities could be provided.

From the beginning, girl pupils helped to do laundry work, but in those early days nurses also worked in the laundry. They apparently had to rise at 4.00 a.m. to begin washing blankets by treading them in large tubs, with their skirts kilted up to keep them dry.

The laundry that replaced the one lost in the fire was converted into a classroom when a new laundry was built in 1891. This was enlarged and re-equipped twenty years later. By the 1930s it was washing and dressing 10,000 articles a week, but in 1936 the work was transferred to the Colony laundry. It had been planned as a separate unit, but was extended to handle 20,000 items a week from both sites. Soon it was employing about 35 girls and handling

The laundry in the 1920s.

59

an increasing number of articles: 24,000 in 1937, 28,000 in 1939 and 35,000 in 1941. It has been upgraded many times since then, although more recent improvements have had to provide for operation without patient labour.

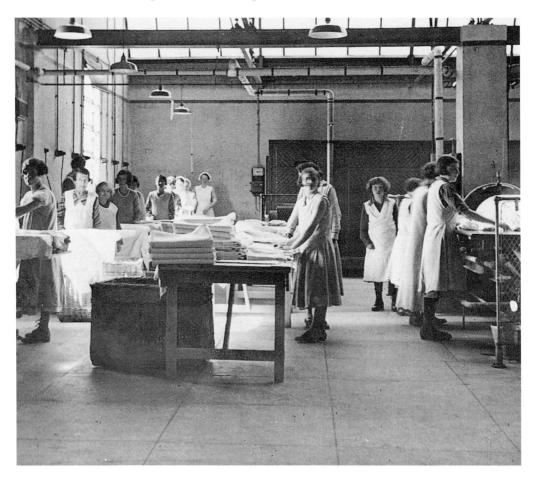

The Colony laundry.

Machines take the strain in the 1990s.

The Industrial Colony

William J. Gibson, the architect of the nurses' home at the juvenile site (and Falkirk Royal Infirmary), designed the main Colony buildings . The hospital and nursing villas, were designed by James Millar and a third architect, Alexander Black, designed the workshops, farm and alterations to the gate lodges: his Falkirk practice of A & W Black had worked on developments at the Institution since 1871!

The administration block was built in a square, enclosing a courtyard. The offices and boardroom were on the south side of the ground floor with matron's quarters in the west corner. Along the west side were sitting rooms for nurses and assistant matrons, a reading room and a visitors' room. The central kitchen, and the dining rooms, for nurses and maids, were on the north side and along the east corridor was a visitors room, a maids' recreation room and storekeeper's accommodation. The assistant medical officer's quarters were in the south-east corner. The first floor had 42 bedrooms for nurses and maids and there were more bedrooms on the top floor, but they were not fitted out until 1937.

The ground floor of each of the five main villas was taken up with a dining room, two day rooms, cloakroom, toilets and staff duty room. Above, there were two eighteen-bedded dormitories, two smaller rooms for six and eight people and two rooms for staff. The villas and administration block all faced south.

North of the administration block was the recreation hall, and to the north of it were buildings containing the kitchens, laundry, store rooms, pumps and boilers. To the west of the boiler house were the male patients' workshops and about 200 yards further west were smaller workrooms for the women. The hospital and nursing villas were to the east of the main buildings.

The Colony from the east.

Unmarried male staff had to live in any space that could be found, including rooms in the villas, and the hospital before it was commissioned. Their nomadic existence ended in 1939 when a hostel was opened. It had a dining room, recreation room and twelve bedrooms. An extension of twelve more bedrooms was planned, but never built because the men who left for war service were replaced by married men who lived at home.

Day room.

Recreation hall.

Stores.

The male staff hostel in its later guise as Morven ward.

Boys being taught gardening skills outside the covered playground.

Girls tending the old Institution's gardens.

Farms and Gardens

In the second half of the nineteenth century, mental health institutions were sited in the countryside, where they could run their own farms to provide therapeutic occupation for adult patients and a supply of food. While this rural isolation doubtless benefited hospitals like Bellsdyke, it had disadvantages for the Institution. The children were young and often too frail to be used for profitable work, and it was difficult to occupy their minds through the long, dark, winter evenings. Nevertheless, the Institution had some land, and a gardener was employed to maintain it and teach boys gardening skills. They grew a variety of vegetable crops, like potatoes, cabbages, carrots, parsnips and beetroot. Flowers for decorating the rooms were grown in a conservatory which was replaced by a new, larger one in 1890. Some livestock like chickens and pigs were also kept. The gardener and children also tended the Superintendent's private garden. It had some fine fruit trees which provided the Institution with apples, pears and plums.

The two farms on Larbert Estate were made into one, centred on Househill Farm to the west of Larbert House. It was used mainly as a dairy farm with a herd of tuberculin-free Ayrshire cows. They supplied most of the milk needed by the residents and staff at both juvenile and Colony sites. There were two byres with 20 stalls each, electric milkers, wash-hand basins and individual water bowls for the cows. Between the byres was a central area for storage and

The new byre at Househill Farm.

Girls on the poultry farm.

Sizing potatoes.

Tattie howking – whole wards of residents were mobilised to provide a labour force when the potatoes were ready for lifting.

Gathering crops.

preparation of feed-stuffs. There was also a milk house, scullery and boiler house with sterilising plant for milk cans.

The farm grew grain crops and root vegetables, and 2,000 free-range chickens laid all the eggs that the Institution needed. Mutton, pork and bacon came from the farm's own animals, and beef cattle were reared for a time. The stock and produce won cups and commendations at agricultural shows.

A wide variety of produce was grown in the Colony gardens, including enough soft fruit to make about two tons of jam a year. The financial saving to the Institution was considerable and some crops made a profit. Tomatoes, peaches, grapes, cucumbers and chrysanthemums, were all cultivated for sale on the open market. The extensive estate woodlands also provided employment and some revenue.

The gardens and farm continued to provide patient employment for a time under the NHS although the range of produce was narrower. Househill Farm was the last hospital farm in Scotland when it was sold in the early 1980s. But instead of ending the tradition of patients working on the land, some of the money from the sale was used to set up a Horticultural Therapy Unit.

Making hay.

At the hay shed.

The walled garden and glasshouses at Larbert House were used like a market garden to grow fruit and vegetables.

Inside the glasshouses.

Christmas Trees and Summer Treats

The annual Christmas festival was always special – even if, in the early years, it was held in January. Evergreen branches, paper chains and Chinese lanterns were hung from the Gothic rafters of the dining hall, and it was also decorated with children's pictures, needlework and knitting. Bible messages were pinned to the walls. A large Christmas tree, illuminated by small candles, was placed at the end of the hall and hung with presents. The children entertained the dignitaries with carols and songs, including action songs, and gave displays of drill or dancing. Some children also performed solo, in duets, or played musical instruments. The dignitaries made speeches! After tea, the presents were distributed and the hall reverberated to the sounds of tambourines, drums and whistles as delighted children played with their new toys. Each child was also given a treat, like an orange – a rarity in those days!

More than one Christmas tree was needed to hold the larger number of presents and fill the covered playground, when the festival moved in there. Changing times were also reflected in the children's performances. The latest 'Swedish drill' was on display in 1911, along with a patriotic pageant in which children paraded for the invited guests in costumes representing the countries of the British Isles and 'Colonial Volunteers'. They ended by singing 'Rule Britannia' and 'God Save the King'. Sometimes disease and the risk of cross-infection curtailed the celebrations, but the children got their presents anyway. During the First World War the festival became more of a children's party, with the adult guests refraining from making speeches – perhaps the children preferred it that way! Gramophone music was played, and at least one party ended with a 'cinematograph entertainment' provided by Lizar's of Glasgow.

The second highlight in the children's year was the summer outing. It took the form of a picnic with outdoor games, a sing-song and rambles. The venue changed from time to time. In 1870 it was a field in the Carron Valley and, for a few years in the 1890s, Mr and Mrs Claude Hamilton invited the children to Dunmore Park, and also gave them presents. Other picnic locations included Hopetoun House, Blackness and Doune Castle: 200 children piled into horse-drawn brakes to go to Doune in 1906. They

Santa hands out presents at a Christmas party in the covered playground, with Dr Spence looking on.

had tea in the castle and spent an hour playing games outside before setting out for home through Dunblane and Bridge of Allan. The tired but happy children arrived back at 9.00 p.m.

Long days were not unusual. When Campsie Glen was the favoured destination in 1910, the horse-brakes left Larbert at 10.00 a.m. and took about four hours to reach the spot where the children rambled, picnicked and played games until 5.00 p.m. On the return journey they stopped for refreshments, arriving back at 9.00 p.m. Bad weather caused the 1912 outing to Doune to be cancelled twice and the third time almost proved unlucky too. Heavy rain soaked everyone before the packed open brakes reached Stirling, but an approach to the Stirling Picture Palace saved the day. They put on films, and entertained the children so well that no-one minded not going to Doune.

Motor charabancs were used for the summer outing in 1916, but the annual picnic ended its nomadic days in the early 1920s when Sir John H. N. Graham allowed a field on Larbert estate to be used. This arrangement continued until the estate was bought for the Colony, after which the activities spread over a number of fields! The Colony residents' early outings were by motor bus to the seaside at Gullane or Aberdour, but in 1938 they went in small groups to the Empire Exhibition at Bellahouston Park in Glasgow. They were given pocket money and some freedom to roam, but all returned safely. Children also went to the Falkirk Tryst fair where the show-people gave them free rides.

Outings have continued over the years to country or seaside destinations and to places like Blair Drummond Safari Park, Butlins at Ayr, Culzean Castle and Falkland Palace. Evening visits to the Hillfoots, Culross and other nearby locations have also been popular, as have trips to events like Prestwick Air Show, the Edinburgh Military Tattoo and, with complimentary tickets provided by the Scottish Football Association, to international football matches.

A picnic in the grounds of Larbert House in the 1930s.

Recreation

Winter evenings were always harder to fill in the early days. Skipping, dancing, reading and a variety of household games like marbles, solitaire and dominoes were used to occupy the time. The drill hall, described in the 1870s as ' a lofty apartment with an imitation stage' was also used as a concert room and theatre. Staff put on performances, charades and musical entertainments – hard going for them, but a source of delight to the children, some of whom also liked to take part. On occasions, children would perform their own little plays. They also enjoyed making music and putting on concerts. In the late 1930s their percussion bands and country dancing teams were entered, with some success, in competitions at the Central Counties Musical Festival at Falkirk.

Percussion band in the covered playground.

Entertainers gave freely of their time in the early days, including the Messrs Dailly, well-known amateur magicians from Dundee, who amused the children and guests in 1887. Other performers included ventriloquists, conjurors and the Larbert Tennessee Boys who put on a minstrel show. One of the directors, Major Nimmo, gave magic lantern presentations, and concerts were given by choirs from Larbert and Stenhousemuir. Films and television curtailed such activities, but choirs and other entertainers continued to visit the children. Sometimes a third party helped, as in 1972, when a Christmas puppet show was sponsored by Forth Valley Junior Chamber of Commerce.

Percussion bands and country dancers won certificates at the Central Counties Musical Festival.

The paddling pool was an instant success.

Sand pit.

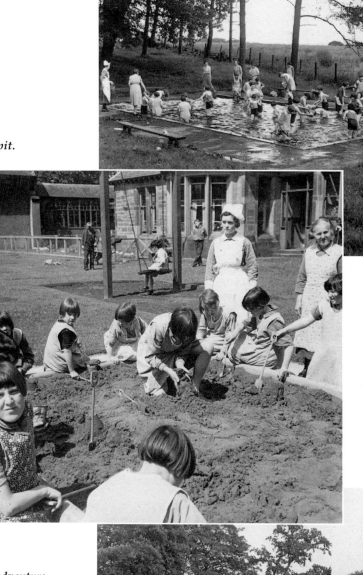

This adventure playground was set up at the juvenile site in 1975. A donation from Larbert Round Table paid for the superchute and much of the construction work was done by boys from the Polmont 'Borstal'.

72

About ninety children went to the pantomime in Falkirk, for the first time, in 1920. After that, visits to the theatre became a regular part of life for both juvenile and adult residents.

Self-produced live entertainment was still the order of the day in the 1940s and 50s when staff staged concert parties in the Colony hall. They performed as singers, musicians and comedians, to the amusement of residents and colleagues alike. The staff Concert and Dramatic Club also performed in competitions, with some success.

Early functions, like the children's Christmas festival, were often followed by tea and 'a short list of dances' for staff and guests. These developed into an annual staff dance which went on until the early hours of the morning and was clearly a social highlight. In the early years of the twentieth century the music was provided by Mr Binnie's Orchestra, or, as it was better known, Binnie's Band from Stenhousemuir. In the 1920s the Fitz Orchestra wowed the customers and in November 1934 the recreation hall resounded to the strains of Bobby Richardson's band. The function on that occasion included a whist drive, fancy dress parade and dance. In later years the Colony hall was used for monthly staff dances, Young Farmers' Club dances and weekly residents' dances. In the 1970s student volunteers from Stirling University helped nursing staff with weekly patients' social evenings.

Birthday, Hallowe'en or special tea parties were held in the day rooms and children were allowed to eat as much as was good for them and, as a special treat, to stay up a little later. Sometimes a child's parents would send a cake which would be the cue for a party. Hallowe'en dances and fancy dress parades were also enjoyed by adult residents and in the 1970s a special Hallowe'en and bonfire night display by Larbert Round Table included gymnastic displays and a sing-along.

Radio Royal's first newsletter.

Gramophones and records were bought in 1912 with surplus money from the Christmas festival. They were so popular that more had to be purchased – and replaced when the old ones wore out. Radio was installed in the 1930s and loudspeakers were placed in the hall, and all the accommodation blocks; programmes of Scottish country dance music were the most popular! Every villa was provided with a 'radiogram' in the 1960s and nursing staff could choose what they wanted to play from a record library. Radio Royal, a hospital radio station for Falkirk hospitals, was set up in the main building about 1980. The presenters and technicians also provided music and a public address system at open days.

Visits from travelling 'cinematograph shows' ceased when a film projector was

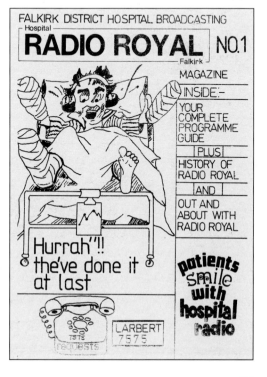

Ring-a-roses at the girls' playground.

Boys' playground.

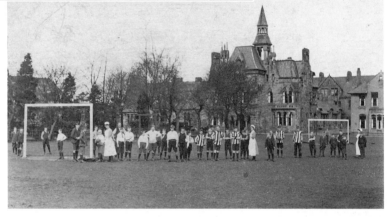

Hockey team, c.1930.

74

donated in 1924. It was very popular with the children. The Colony's hall had a projector room, and the back wall of the stage was painted as a screen, but the shortage of silent films and the high cost of talkies meant that there were no movies for the early residents. Sound projectors were installed at the Colony and juvenile sites in 1936 and weekly shows were put on at both throughout the winter months.

Swings were always popular with younger children, although some needed help to make them swing. Six new swings, sand pits, a see-saw, and a paddling pool came into use at the juvenile site in 1936. The pool was so successful that a large number of bathing costumes had to be bought. The children usually went for a walk on Saturdays. Sometimes a hundred or more formed up behind the engineer. He was a good piper and played marching tunes as the column walked over to Plean for a picnic.

Summer games in the early days consisted of cricket for the boys and croquet for the girls. Later, football became the boys' main outdoor sport. Boys took to the concept of team games better than girls who seemed to prefer individual activities like skipping and dancing, although hockey and netball teams were later formed. By the 1920s the football team was playing local Boy Scout and Boys Brigade teams, while the hockey team played against other

Football team, 1938.

Netball team.

Drill with Indian clubs.

Bowling green with Ard and Brora villas behind.

schools. To begin with the teams tended to be 'beaten but not disgraced', but fortunes had clearly improved when it was reported that they 'sometimes win'! The main football pitch was on the parkland across the road from the main gate. In later years, as transport improved and residents got older, sports like bowls and football were organised into leagues with games being played against patients from mental hospitals. Some men also took part in a local domino league and there was a billiard table in most adult male villas. Staff supported the residents in these activities and enjoyed their own games of darts, badminton, football and bowls. A new sports pavilion was erected beside the playing fields in the 1970s.

Other group activities included a Girl Guide Company, the 1st Torwood, which was formed with twelve girls in 1939 and lasted for about thirty years. A special company of the Boys' Brigade, the 4th Larbert, was set up in the early 1940s with boys from the Institution and some from the neighbourhood. They went for summer camps and held open days where they put on displays of gymnastics and drill – the drill team won prizes in open competition.

National celebrations provided a wonderful break from routine. Firework displays and bonfires, topped with 'appropriate effigies', marked the wartime victory days VE Day and VJ Day. Visits were also arranged to the Stenhousemuir Picture Palace. Each child was given a souvenir of the coronation of King George VI in 1937, and two days of sports were held. Another sports day was held, in brilliant sunshine, to celebrate Queen Elizabeth's coronation in 1953 and more souvenirs were handed out. A matinee film show at the Stenhousemuir Picture Palace was also laid on for some residents who each received a free tub of ice cream.

Girls' costume race.

Obstacle race.

Taking a tumble from
the greasy pole.

Television had arrived in Scotland just before the coronation and many of the residents were able to view the event live. They were no doubt as much in awe of the new-fangled form of entertainment as by what it showed. By the 1960s there was a television set in every villa, which kept residents entertained for hours on end, but, as in society as a whole, other forms of occupation and amusement suffered!

'Pets Corner' was one form of amusement that survived television. There were rabbits, guinea pigs, cockatoos, budgies, chickens and other creatures, and, at the juvenile site, a pony called Silver. On the Colony site the pets were housed in a large wooden hut. It was demolished to make way for the Inver wards, but not before its concrete foundations, reinforced with old iron bedsteads, had tested the ingenuity and patience of the contractors.

Residents took part in a number of European Special Olympics events. The Central Region team for the event at Glasgow's Celtic Park in 1990 is seen here outside RSNH. It included four residents who won two gold medals, a silver and a bronze.

Holidays

Holidays were always part of the early Institution's culture, with about one in three of the children able to go home to their families, or to friends, for two weeks' vacation in the summer, and at New Year. Just before the First World War, some of the private patients were taken, as an experiment, to a rented house at Garelochhead for a holiday. It was so successful that holiday houses were taken in succeeding summers on the Clyde Coast and in Strathyre. After the Second World War, female patients went for two-week holidays to a British Legion hall at Pittenweem. The men went camping at locations like Kinlochard and Callander, but within a few years they appeared to give up on the hassle and hazards of the open-air and they too spent summer holidays in halls on the Fife coast.

The attractions of sleeping under canvas returned with an annual ritual known as 'Callander Camp'. Large tents for the residents and smaller ones for staff were pitched on a site near the Bracklinn Falls in early summer and not taken down until the autumn. Creature comforts came in the form of old iron bedsteads, a single stand pipe for cold water and home cooking by the nursing staff! Muirfield House, on the East Lothian coast, was bought in 1969 for use as an extension of the hospital – patients spent two weeks there; the change was as good as a holiday! Later, some groups of residents went farther afield, to Blackpool, Jersey and even to Spain. And the wheel turned full circle in 1990 when Strathyre was again the destination for some residents and staff who went on an activity holiday to Bailefuil Outdoor Resident Centre.

Walking in the hills.

Open Days

Open days contained elements of summer sports and sales of work. They developed during the NHS time into annual features of both adult and juvenile hospitals. They were fun, and helped to promote the hospital and raise funds. There were visits from pipe bands and police dogs, and displays by Scottish country dancers, majorettes and model aeroplanes. Competition included tug-o-war, five-a-side football and bowls. Other attractions included a fortune teller, fancy dress parades, balloon races, 'Beat the Goalie' and 'Duck the Lady'. In this sadistic activity a student nurse was dropped into four feet of water every time someone hit a target; her target was to raise lots of money. Wards set up their own stalls to sell cakes and candy, ice cream and lemonade, teas, books, garden produce and raffle tickets.

The balloons go up at an open day.

Open day activity.

*'Silver' takes
children for a ride in
a trap at a juvenile
site open day.*

Staff

All staff in the early Institution, including the nurses, cooks, laundresses, housemaids, gardener, and carpenter had to assist in teaching life-skills to the children. They and the teachers had to exercise great patience, self control and skill in doing their job. Working hours were long and recreation curtailed. The gates were locked at 10.00 p.m. and anyone not back in was in trouble. The engineer, who lived in the lodge, had the task of locking the gate, and young nurses and maids going for a night out would implore him to keep it unlocked for as long as possible. His working day started at 6.00 a.m. and finished when he damped down the boilers at night and shut the gate.

Despite these apparent stresses the Institution became something of a 'family firm' with generations of many families working there. Shifts were often adjusted so that married couples could have time off together.

The Medico- (later Royal Medico-) Psychological Association recognised the Institution as a training school for their nursing certificate in 1912. A few years later the Association introduced a new certificate in mental deficiency nursing, and staff were encouraged to gain the qualification. A nurse training school was set up and it regularly attracted over 50 student nurses a year. All nurses were female until male staff were needed for the adult male residents at the Colony. After the NHS was set up, a joint nurse training school was established in the 'base camp' wartime huts at Bellsdyke Mental Hospital to serve both hospitals. Nurses could qualify as either a Registered Mental Nurse (RMN) or Registered Nurse for the Mentally Handicapped (RNMH).

Nurses outside the Institution.

Staff had to try to bring back any residents who wandered, or ran, off: certified people with a mental handicap could discharge themselves 'by escape' if they left and stayed away for three months. Nurses in full uniform gave chase across fields and public roads, while one Physician Superintendent, in hot pursuit of a fleeing child, tore the seat of his trousers on a barbed wire fence. With an expert tailor on staff, his dignity was perhaps a greater casualty than the pants!

Retaining staff during the two world wars was difficult, but the larger number of people needed by the Colony meant that the problem was worse during the Second World War. Older staff were kept on past retirement age. Recruitment almost dried up in the mid-1940s and staff shortages enforced a heavy working week. Day and night shifts were of twelve hours' duration and, for the

Nurses outside the first nurses' home.

In a dining room.

charge nurses, they were extended to include a hand-over to the incoming shift. In those days, nurses had to clean the wards and windows, polish the floors and brass pipes, and wash down toilet walls. Soiled sheets had to be pre-washed in the 'slunge room' before being sent to the laundry. Spring-cleaning meant taking all the mattresses off the beds and carrying them downstairs to air outside on the grass.

Staffing problems returned in the early 1950s, despite higher salaries and the promise of reduced hours. The Institution was functioning with 54 fewer nurses than before the war, and had only one or two junior nurses attending to a ward or villa instead of pre-war numbers of up to six. People could not be released for lectures and tutorials, which made nurse training difficult. A number of ex-servicemen were recruited as nurses, as were some Polish people who remained in Scotland after the war. The staff-to-patient ratio improved, but returned to low levels as patient numbers rose through the late 1950s and 60s.

As part of the centenary celebrations in 1963, the staff were treated to dinner and entertainment in the Dobbie Hall. Half of the staff went on one night, with a second sitting on another evening for the other half.

For the barber, high patient numbers in the 1960s and 70s meant that cutting the men's hair was like painting the Forth Bridge. Despite attending to 30 men or boys in a day, it took so long to get around all the patients it was time to start again when the last one was finished. The barber also attended to patients at Muirfield House, travelling there by train and bus.

A voluntary services organiser was appointed in 1981 to co-ordinate voluntary activities and strengthen ties with the community. Two nurses in Beauly ward won a Scotland-wide NHS staff suggestions competition in 1989 with the development of a continence cushion known as the 'Beauly Cushion'. It looked like a domestic cushion and gave patients a sense of dignity and comfort. The hospital's Nursing and Catering Services also received recognition in 1994, when they both gained accredited standards certification.

Nursing staff at a children's picnic.

Directors and Associates of the Early Institution

Some very prominent Scots were associated with the Institution. Sir James Young Simpson, who discovered the anaesthetic properties of chloroform, was a Vice-President. More than one generation of the Coats family of Paisley, famous for thread-making, were Vice-Presidents or Directors and alongside them on the Board were members of the Pullar family of Perth Dyeworks. Directors drawn from the world of shipping and shipbuilding included a number of the Denny family of Dumbarton, Henry Lithgow of the Kingston Shipbuilding Yard, Port Glasgow, and Sir Alexander Gracie of the Fairfield Shipbuilding Company of Govan. Lord Inverclyde of Cunard was a Vice-President. The most distinguished representative from the world of politics was Sir Henry Campbell-Bannerman who was a Vice-President of the Institution before he became the nation's Prime Minister in 1906.

The Duchess of Montrose.

Many landed ladies and gentlemen gave freely of their time and money including the Earl and Countess of Mar and Kellie, and the Duchess of Montrose who was associated with other Societies dealing with mental deficiency. The Marquis of Zetland, whose forebears developed the Forth & Clyde Canal, was Honorary President for some years. Others like Lord and Lady Overtoun, who owed their wealth and position to the proceeds of industry, were equally supportive.

Local industrialists and landowners were also prominent, and officiated at many functions. Major Dobbie, founder of the Larbert Stove and Iron Works, took a very active interest until his death in 1908. Others included James Wilson of South Bantaskin, William Forbes of Callendar House, Colonel Nimmo of Westquarter, Robert Hunter of Glenfuir and of course Sir John H. N. Graham of Larbert House.

Ladies' Auxiliaries

Some of the most effective fund-raising was done by groups of women known as Ladies' Auxiliaries. They were formed, usually after public meetings and, once established, set about collecting money. They held bazaars (sales of work, accompanied by music and entertainments) and generally busied themselves cajoling friends, neighbours and members of the public to support the institution's work. The first group was formed in Edinburgh, but the ladies of Glasgow were the more aggressive fund-raisers. They divided the city into districts and organised a network of house-to-house collectors – and a visit from one these determined West End or South Side ladies must have been daunting, and hard to resist. Within a few years of the Institution opening, Auxiliaries were operating in all major centres, and meetings were being held to extend the network to towns and villages across the country.

Secretary and Treasurer A. J. Fitch was responsible for setting up these Ladies' Auxiliaries. He was a familiar sight at the Institution and his great white beard helped to establish for him a 'foster father' image. The beard was not always white: when he retired in 1912 he had been working for the Institution for 51 years!

Bands, like this, entertained guests at various functions.

Funds and Gifts

The charitable Institution was an aggressive fund-raiser and in its lifetime set up a variety of special funds and appeals. These allowed finances to be kept separate and ensured that there was always money to pay staff and maintain buildings. Care was taken not to embark on a development project without having the money to pay for it. Extensions to buildings in the 1860s and 70s were financed by separate appeals, as were special projects like the covered playground and hospitals. Almost as soon as the Institution was occupied, Mrs Brodie took personal charge of a Fences and Lodge Fund to pay for securing the boundaries. The fences were erected, but the lodge had to wait.

A special investment fund was set up in 1879 and efforts to raise a minimum of £10,000 for it began. The objective was to invest the money, to provide a regular income to pay for salaries and other necessities. By the end of 1883, £8,000 had been subscribed and the fund reached its target figure two years later. Subsequent legacies and other donations were added to it. Much of the money was invested in railway stocks; highly appropriate for an Institution dependent on the railway for its daily needs!

Smaller funds were set up to provide additional comforts. 'The thank-offering of Parents for Intelligent Children' provided a useful source of money for little extras, while the Christmas Tree Fund paid for the seasonal festivities in winter and summer.

As well as these donations, the Institution received numerous gifts. Christmas trees and presents for the children were received every year. Unusual items like 21 brace of grouse, a goat, barrels of American apples, boxes of oranges and sets of croquet, figured amongst the more obvious rocking horses, dolls, toys, books, barley sugar and sponge cakes. And even after the NHS had taken over, individuals and charitable organisations continued to donate money for toys, equipment and ward funds.

War

Wars created problems for an Institution whose work had to continue regardless of what was going on in the outside world. During the First World War shortages of basic supplies developed and costs doubled. Coal consumption rose because the quality available for non-industrial use was very poor. Larbert was alive with soldiers because of its proximity to the railway. The Stenhousemuir trysting ground was used as a transit camp, and some troops even camped on the ground across the road from the Institution's main gate. Soldiers often marched past, to the great excitement of the children.

A few of the Institution's former pupils enlisted. One boy saw action in Gallipoli, Palestine and France and seemed almost proud of his nickname 'Daft Charlie'. He was wounded twice and left with a good service record. Another boy, who had been difficult to teach because of retarded development, had joined up and served as a transport driver. During the German advance in 1918 he showed so much courage in evacuating the wounded he was awarded the Military Medal.

On the outbreak of the Second World War, two young men managed to discharge themselves by escape and join the army, but three others were returned. More land was ploughed up as the nation was exhorted to 'dig for victory' and some farm produce was requisitioned. The sewing room came into its own salvaging torn clothes and linen, and returning them to use. All children were fitted with gas masks. A motor-trailer fire pump was bought for emergencies. It was manned by tradesmen, but with so few staff living on site some of the Colony boys had to be trained in the use of stirrup pumps. Windows had to be blacked out, which was not easy for the kitchen and laundry roof lights. Baffle walls were built in front of entrance doors, and every villa had a protected ground floor room where the windows were encased in wood and filled with sand. In one 'emergency' 180 boys and their attendants grabbed their blankets and gas masks and made their way to the shelter rooms, only to discover that a fifteen-year-old boy had mimicked the air-raid siren!

Repairing torn clothes and bedding helped the Institution through two world wars.

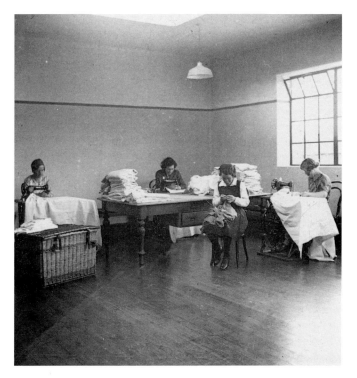

Fire

Late one January evening, within months of the Institution opening, the wooden laundry building went up in flames. The fire, which was thought to have been caused by an overheated stove, was noticed by a farmer. There was no organised brigade in those days and so about 60 local men rushed to tackle the blaze. At one point the fire threatened the main buildings, but the volunteers managed to contain it and by the early hours of the following morning had it under control. A few items of laundry were saved, but the building was destroyed.

The shock of losing the building was compounded for the directors when they discovered that it was uninsured. The laundry had been built as a separate structure with the intention of connecting it to the main buildings, but the linking block had not been built and the separate laundry should have had separate insurance. The North British and Mercantile Insurance Company, however, accepted the directors' plea that it had been an unintentional oversight, and agreed to pay!

The sanatorium was damaged by fire in 1907. An airborne spark from the furnace chimney was thought to have lodged under the roof slates of the upper storey nurses' quarters. The damage was extensive and the building was out of use for five months while repairs were carried out.

A 30,000 gallon storage tank was installed, just before the First World War, to provide an emergency water supply for fire fighting. A separate fire main was also put in around the buildings and a stationary steam-powered fire engine was installed in the boiler house. It could pump water at a rate of 400 gallons a minute over any part of the buildings.

Direct telephone communication with Falkirk Fire Brigade was installed in 1954 and fire engines were called to a number of minor outbreaks. A fire appliance, manned by a part time crew of male nurses and tradesmen was based at Bellsdyke Hospital in 1972. It was intended to deal with fires at Bellsdyke, both RSNH sites and Health Board houses until the full-time brigade arrived. The crew were given a special dispensation to take their appliance onto public roads to attend to emergencies.

In 1985 the hospital radio service, Radio Royal, actually announced one blaze on air when smoke from a burning mattress filled the corridor outside their studio. Central Region Fire Brigade were called to a different kind of emergency in December 1994 when heavy rain caused flooding throughout central Scotland. Patients in Morar and Solway wards were evacuated, but the brigade prevented the need for further action.

Opposite:
The fire-engine based at Bellsdyke Hospital.

Scottish Central Railway

The Scottish Central Railway was just that – central. When it was promoted in the 1840s many people saw it as a bad investment. Its route from an empty field at Greenhill, near High Bonnybridge, through Larbert, Stirling and Dunblane to the small city of Perth was less than 60 miles long and unlikely to attract much custom. But its backers had vision and when their railway was completed in 1848 it formed a vital link between the north and south of the country. As the network developed, Greenhill became an important junction with the Caledonian Railway's line from Carlisle and the cross-country Edinburgh and Glasgow Railway. Perth became a prosperous railway town and a hub for routes to the north. In those pioneering railway days the 'Central' became a big company. It owned the only railway bridge over the Forth, at Stirling, and was able to form lucrative financial agreements with other railway companies. But in the mid 1860s, the Edinburgh-based North British Railway and Glasgow's Caledonian Railway began to dominate the industry, swallowing up many smaller companies. The Scottish Central became part of the Caledonian's system on 1st August 1865. In the great railway amalgamations of the 1920s the Caledonian became part of the London Midland and Scottish Railway (LMS) which was nationalised in 1948. The 'bad investment' of the 1840s has since survived the Beeching cuts of the 1960s and privatisation in the 1990s to remain an essential link in the country's railway system.

Bellsdyke Hospital

The Stirling District Asylum was along the road to the east of the original Institution. It was set up by Stirling District Lunacy Board which had been established under the Lunacy (Scotland) Act of 1857. The Board had responsibility for the mentally ill people of Stirlingshire, Clackmannan, Dunbartonshire and Linlithgowshire (West Lothian), and had the unenviable task of finding a site for an asylum to cater for this scattered area. Larbert, with its excellent rail connections, proved to be the ideal location and in 1859 the Board acquired a 74-acre site, but waited for clarification of the lunacy laws before building.

Plans were approved by 1866 and it was hoped to open the new asylum on Whitsunday 1868, but problems with water and gas supplies delayed the opening until February 1869. The patients came from the lunatic wards of poorhouses in Stirling, Linlithgow and Dumbarton, and the old Falkirk Parochial Asylum, which was closed down when the new asylum was opened.

The asylum became a Naval Hospital during the First World War and was used again by the military authorities during World War Two, with huts in the grounds known as the 'base camp'. As time went on, the title was changed to Bellsdyke Mental Hospital and finally to Bellsdyke Hospital. A 1953 proposal to amalgamate the administrative structures of the Larbert hospitals was summarily dismissed by the RSNI Board of Management. They believed that the Institution was big enough to warrant separate management, and was likely to get bigger. Nevertheless administrative links were made and a joint Board of Management for the 'Larbert Hospitals' was set up in 1972.

Male sanatorium at the Stirling District Asylum, c.1905.

MALE SANATORIUM. S.D.A. LARBERT.

Silent Witnesses

Ancient trees on the Woodland Walk.

The great hospitals, drawn to Larbert because of its unique combination of relative isolation and good railway connections, are progressively closing and giving up their land. This is feeding a transformation of the area based, not on the railway, but on the now excellent motorway connections. The structures on the old juvenile site have mostly gone now, although the original 'Pilkington' house, a ward block and the lodge remain, and may yet be restored to add character to the new housing and commercial developments springing up around them. Some buildings on the old Larbert Estate site may also be kept standing and act as reminders to future generations of the part the hospital played in the development of social thinking in Scotland. As ever, the true legacy is in the way people's lives have changed, not the landscape, but the many beautiful trees, that were growing on the estate before the Colony was set up, will hopefully survive; silent witnesses to a remarkable story.

A dining room, thought to be in the New Block
of 1907, and used by private, fee-paying, boys.

Opposite:
Girls' playground.

Acknowledgements

Working in and around the hospital has brought me into contact with many people who have shown great interest in the project. I hope the finished product meets their expectations. A number of people have helped with the book and I must thank Dr Derek Sinclair, Dr David Primrose, Bill Gent, Kate McKeown, Jean and Danny McRoberts, Jimmy Bell, Ian Aitken, Nancy McKechnie, Esther Anderson, Durward Sinclair, Alex Muirhead, Anne Hawkins, Bobbie Dickie and Tom Horne for access to their memories. I enjoyed the few days I spent in Medical Records and must thank the staff there who treated me kindly, as a guest, and also helped with some useful observations.

I must thank Falkirk Museums for use of the picture on page 87, Andrew Fenton for the picture on page 91, Margo Ritchie for the newscuttings on page 22, Dr David Primrose for the pictures on pages 38 (middle), 73, and 82 (lower) and Jean McRoberts for the picture on page 49. All other pictures are the property of the hospital.

Katherine Novosel had the unenviable task of keeping me supplied with archive and photographic material. A history can't be written without the raw material, so I must thank her for sticking to the task when trails seemed to go cold.

The resources of Falkirk Library were invaluable, in particular the microfilmed back-numbers of the *Falkirk Herald*. I must thank the library staff for their unfailing courtesy and good humour. Thanks, too, to the local history research staff at Callendar House for their help.

Also by Guthrie Hutton:
Gartloch Hospital: 100 Years
published by: Stenlake Publishing, Ayrshire KA18 2NX.

Woodilee Hospital: 125 Years
Leverndale Hospital: 100 Years (written in collaboration with Dr Kenneth Binns)
published by: Greater Glasgow Community and Mental Health Services NHS Trust,
G12 0XH. (Now Greater Glasgow Primary Care NHS Trust)